Sewanee
A to Z

by Katie Hines Porterfield

Illustrated by Bob Askew

Katie Hines Porterfield

Bob Askew

Dear Don and Quentin,

For you to enjoy together and to say thank you Don for your friendship and gifts over the years — Bob

acknowledgements

Special thanks to my cousin, Robin Jones (C'98), and his wife, Amanda Plauché Jones (C'98), who recognized the need for a Sewanee children's book and trusted me to make it a reality. Without their foresight and creative assistance, this book never would have happened. I also want to thank Michael Burgin (C' 90) for his editorial advice.

Many thanks to my dear, talented friend, Laura Deleot (C'96) of Crookston Design for her design and publishing expertise. In addition to providing the unmatched skill and professionalism that she brings to every project, she designed this book with the discerning eye of a Sewanee alumnus. Laura, I am deeply indebted to you.

To my illustrator, Bob Askew: Thank you for joining me on this journey. Only someone intimately familiar with (and equally as appreciative of) Sewanee could have captured these scenes. Your dedication and perfectionism were also welcome additions to the project.

Bob and I are extremely grateful to Ben Potter, another talented artist out of Sewanee, whose whimsical, copper, and tin "Sewanee Angels" inspired the angels in this book.

Finally, thank you Mom and Dad for giving me the opportunity to discover this magical place. And last but certainly not least, to my best friend and husband, Forrest, who I met at Sewanee so many years ago. Thank you for your unwavering love and support.

For S&H. May you find your "Sewanee"
and appreciate it as much as your
dad and I appreciate ours.

Sewanee A to Z

Requests for permission to make copies of any part of the work should be submitted online at info@ mascotbooks.com or mailed to Mascot Books, 560 Herndon Parkway #120, Herndon, VA 20170.

PRT0214A

Printed in the United States

ISBN-13: 9781620862810
ISBN-10: 1620862816

www.mascotbooks.com

There's just something
about Sewanee;
It's as magical as can be.
Come along, I'll show you;
Let's explore from

A to Z.

Can you find the angel in every picture?

A
is for the Angel who keeps you safe when you're away.

B is for Biking on a beautiful day.

C is for the Chapel and for the big Cross on the bluff.

D is for Dogs that often roam and say, "Ruff, ruff."

E is for Ecce Quam Bonum,
our motto from Psalm 133.

F is for the Fog that rolls in frequently.

G is for Green's View, an overlook that can't be beat.

H is for the Honor Code:
Don't lie, steal, or cheat.

I is for Intramurals,
the sports students play for fun.

J is for Jessie Ball duPont Library with books for everyone.

K is for KA Point, a cliff with a breathtaking view.

L is for Lessons and Carols,
a Christmas time must-do.

M

is for
Morgan's
Steep,
where
students
like to climb.

N is for Nature, which surrounds us all the time.

O is for Order of Gownsmen: Whose gown will you wear?

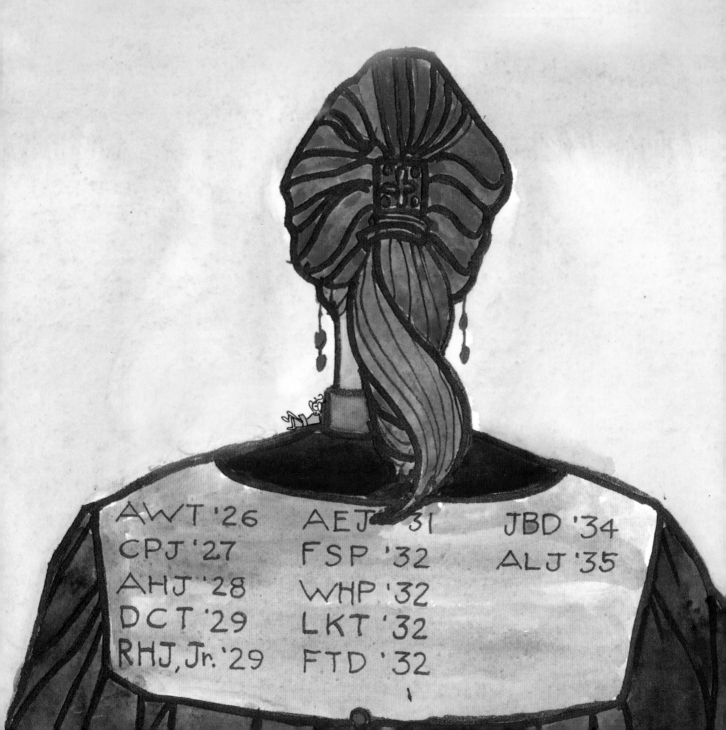

P

is for Perimeter Trail, where
we hike from here to there.

Q is for the Quad, a spot to study and rest your head.

R

is for Rebel's Rest with its roof so red.

S is for Shake Day for those who decide to go Greek.

T

is for Tiger, Sewanee's mascot long and sleek.

THE UNIVERSITY OF THE SOUTH
SEWANEE, TENNESSEE

U is for University of the South,
the more formal of the school's names.

V is for Volunteer Fire Department, whose members put out flames.

W is for Wellingtons who parade with kilt-wearing counterparts.

X marks the spot of a campus that captures hearts.

Y is for "Yea, Sewanee's Right,"
both school motto and old cheer.

Z is for ZZZs that follow
comps senior year.

the end

about the author

A freelance journalist based in Nashville, Tennessee, Katie Hines Porterfield graduated from the University of the South in 1998. She and her husband, Forrest, also C'98, share a house in Sewanee with other alumni and enjoy reminiscing about their college days, while building new memories on the mountain with their twin boys. In addition to her B.A. in American Studies, she holds an M.A. in Journalism from the University of Alabama.

about the artist

Bob Askew specializes in commissioned watercolor and oil paintings. He resides with his wife, Susan, and son, Spears, in Sewanee, Tennessee.
http://www.askewart.com